GW00986054

Management of
health and safety at work

Management of Health and Safety at Work Regulations 1999

APPROVED CODE OF PRACTICE
& GUIDANCE

L21

HSE BOOKS

First published 1992
Second Edition 2000
Reprinted 2000, 2001 (twice), 2002, 2004, 2005

ISBN 0 7176 2488 9

Approved Code of Practice and guidance

This Code has been approved by the Health and Safety
Commission, with the consent of the Secretary of State.
It gives practical advice on how to comply with the law.
If you follow the advice you will be doing enough to comply
with the law in respect of those specific matters on which the
Code gives advice. You may use alternative methods to
those set out in the Code in order to comply with the law.

However, the Code has special legal status. If you are
prosecuted for breach of health and safety law, and it is
proved that you did not follow the relevant provisions of
the Code, you will need to show that you have complied
with the law in some other way or a court will find you at fault.

This document also includes other, more general guidance not
having this special status. This guidance is issued by the Health
and Safety Commission. Following the guidance is not
compulsory and you are free to take other action. But if you do
follow the guidance you will normally be doing enough to comply
with the law. Health and safety inspectors seek to secure
compliance with the law and may refer to this guidance as
illustrating good practice.

The Management of Health and Safety at Work Regulations are
regularly subject to revision and amendment. You should check you
have a copy of the most up-to-date statutory instrument of these
regulations when applying them.

Contents

Editorial note

Since this Approved Code of Practice and Guidance was written, regulation 22 has been amended by the Management of Health and Safety at Work and Fire Precautions (Workplace) (Amendment) Regulations 2003. This amendment came into force from 27th October 2003.

Regulation 22 now reads:

Restriction of civil liability for breach of statutory duty

Breach of a duty imposed on an employer by these Regulations shall not confer a right of action in any civil proceedings insofar as that duty applies for the protection of persons not in his employment.

The amendment to Regulation 22 also alters other Regulations in this Approved Code of Practice and Guidance, as follows:

For Regulation 2 there shall be substituted the following regulation:

Disapplication of these Regulations

(1) These Regulations shall not apply to or in relation to the master or crew of a ship, or to the employer of such persons, in respect of the normal ship-board activities of a ship's crew which are carried out solely by the crew under the direction of the master.

(2) Regulations 3 (4), (5), 10(2) and 19 shall not apply to occasional work or short-term work involving work regarded as not being harmful, damaging or dangerous to young people in a family undertaking.

(3) In this regulation –

"normal ship-board activities" include –

(a) the construction, reconstruction on conversion of a ship outside, but not inside, Great Britain; and

(b) the repair of a ship save repair when carried out in dry dock; "ship" includes every description of vessel used in navigation, other than a ship belonging to Her Majesty which forms part of Her Majesty's Navy".

In Regulation 3 (3) the words "and where" to the end shall follow and not appear in subparagraph (b).

Regulation 19 (4) shall be omitted.

Foreword

This document contains advice on how to comply with duties under the Management of Health and Safety at Work Regulations 1999. It contains the regulations themselves, an Approved Code of Practice (ACOP) which gives advice that has a special legal status described on page ii on preferred means of compliance, and more general guidance that does not have this special status on ways to comply with the law. The regulations are shown in italics, the ACOP is bold type, and the guidance is in plain type. The status of the ACOP and guidance material is described on page ii.

The Management of Health and Safety at Work Regulations 1999 revoke and replace the 1992 Regulations of the same title. This ACOP replaces that associated with the 1992 Regulations.

Notice of Approval

By virtue of Section 16(4) of the Health and Safety at Work etc Act 1974, and with the consent of the Secretary of State for the Environment, Transport and the Regions, the Health and Safety Commission has on 9 December 1999 approved the Code of Practice entitled *Management of Health and Safety at Work*.

The Code of Practice is approved for the purposes of providing practical guidance with respect to the requirements of the Management of Health and Safety at Work Regulations 1999. The Code of Practice comes into effect on 29 December 1999.

Signed

ROSEMARY BANNER
Secretary of Health and Safety Commission

16 December 1999

1   The original Management of Health and Safety at Work Regulations ('the Management Regulations') came into force in 1993[1] as the principal method of implementing the EC Framework Directive (89/391/EEC), adopted in 1989. The Regulations were supported by an Approved Code of Practice. The original Regulations have had to be amended four times since 1992 by the Management of Health and Safety at Work (Amendment) Regulations 1994,[2] which relates to new or expectant mothers, the Health and Safety (Young Persons) Regulations 1997,[3] the Fire Precautions (Workplace) Regulations 1997[4] and by the Management of Health and Safety at Work Regulations 1999.[5] Because the original Regulations have been so significantly amended, they have been revised and published with this new Approved Code of Practice.

2   The Fire Precautions (Workplace) Regulations 1997, as amended by the Fire Precautions (Workplace) (Amendment) Regulations 1999[6] ('the Fire Regulations'), introduced by the Home Office, amend the Management Regulations in several respects. The amendments made by the Fire Regulations make explicit the risk assessment requirement, in so far as it relates to fire safety. They directly require employers to take account of their general fire precautions requirements in Part II of the Fire Regulations (concerning fire-fighting, fire detection, emergency routes and exits and their maintenance) in their assessments. The amendments made by the Fire Regulations affect employers but not self-employed people who do not employ others. The Fire Regulations also introduce:

(a)   a requirement for competent assistance to deal with general fire safety risks;

(b)   a requirement to provide employees with information on fire provisions; and

(c)   a requirement on employers and self-employed people in a shared workplace to co-operate and co-ordinate with others on fire provisions and to provide outside employers with comprehensive information on fire provisions.

See References and Further reading section. Further guidance on fire precautions is available in *Fire safety: An employer's guide*.

3   The duties of the Management Regulations overlap with other regulations because of their wide-ranging general nature. Where duties overlap, compliance with the more specific regulation will normally be sufficient to comply with the corresponding duty in the Management Regulations. For example, the Control of Substances Hazardous to Health Regulations (COSHH) require employers and the self-employed to assess the risks from exposure to substances hazardous to health. An assessment made for the purposes of COSHH will not need to be repeated for the purposes of the Management Regulations. Other instances where overlap may occur include the appointment of people to carry out specific tasks or arrangements for emergencies. However, where the duties in the Management Regulations

[1]S.I. 1992/2051
[2]S.I. 1994/2865
[3]S.I. 1997/135
[4]S.I. 1997/1840
[5]The Management of Health and Safety at Work Regulations 1999 introduced amendments proposed by the Health and Safety (Miscellaneous Modification) Regulations 1999.
[6]S.I. 1999/1877

go beyond those in the more specific regulations, additional measures will be needed to comply fully with the Management of Health and Safety at Work Regulations.

4   Although only the courts can give an authoritative interpretation of law, in considering the application of these regulations and guidance to people working under another's direction, the following should be considered.

5   If people working under the control and direction of others are treated as self-employed for tax and national insurance purposes they may nevertheless be treated as their employees for health and safety purposes. It may therefore be necessary to take appropriate action to protect them. If any doubt exists about who is responsible for the health and safety of a worker this could be clarified and included in the terms of a contract. However, remember, a legal duty under section 3 of the Health and Safety at Work etc Act 1974 (HSW Act)[7] cannot be passed on by means of a contract and there will still be duties towards others under section 3 of HSW Act. If such workers are employed on the basis that they are responsible for their own health and safety, legal advice should be sought before doing so.

6   Words or expressions which are defined in the Management Regulations or in the HSW Act have the same meaning in this Code unless the context requires otherwise.

[7]S.I. 1974 c.37.

Citation, commencement and interpretation

(1)   These Regulations may be cited as the Management of Health and Safety at Work Regulations 1999 and shall come into force on 29th December 1999.

(2)   In these Regulations-

" the 1996 Act" means the Employment Rights Act 1996[a];

"the assessment" means, in the case of an employer or self-employed person, the assessment made or changed by him in accordance with regulation 3;

"child" -

(a)   as respects England and Wales, means a person who is not over compulsory school age, construed in accordance with section 8 of the Education Act 1996[b]; and

(b)   as respects Scotland, means a person who is not over school age, construed in accordance with section 31 of the Education (Scotland) Act 1980[c];

"employment business" means a business (whether or not carried on with a view to profit and whether or not carried on in conjunction with any other business) which supplies persons (other than seafarers) who are employed in it to work for and under the control of other persons in any capacity;

" fixed-term contract of employment" means a contract of employment for a specific term which is fixed in advance or which can be ascertained in advance by reference to some relevant circumstance;

" given birth" means delivered a living child or, after twenty-four weeks of pregnancy, a stillborn child;

" new or expectant mother" means an employee who is pregnant; who has given birth within the previous six months; or who is breastfeeding;

" the preventive and protective measures" means the measures which have been identified by the employer or by the self-employed person in consequence of the assessment as the measures he needs to take to comply with the requirements and prohibitions imposed upon him by or under the relevant statutory provisions and by Part II of the Fire Precautions (Workplace) Regulations 1997[d];

" young person" means any person who has not attained the age of eighteen.

(3)   Any reference in these Regulations to-

(a)   a numbered regulation or Schedule is a reference to the regulation or Schedule in these Regulations so numbered; or

(b)   a numbered paragraph is a reference to the paragraph so numbered in the regulation in which the reference appears.

[a] *1996 c.18.*
[b] *1996 c.56.*
[c] *1980 c.44.*
[d] *S.I. 1997/1840; amended by S.I. 1999/1877*

1

11   A risk assessment should usually involve identifying the hazards present in any working environment or arising out of commercial activities and work activities, and evaluating the extent of the risks involved, taking into account existing precautions and their effectiveness. In this Approved Code of Practice:

(a)   a hazard is something with the potential to cause harm (this can include articles, substances, plant or machines, methods of work, the working environment and other aspects of work organisation);

(b)   a risk is the likelihood of potential harm from that hazard being realised. The extent of the risk will depend on:

   (i)   the likelihood of that harm occurring;

   (ii)   the potential severity of that harm, ie of any resultant injury or adverse health effect; and

   (iii)   the population which might be affected by the hazard, ie the number of people who might be exposed.

12   The purpose of the risk assessment is to help the employer or self-employed person to determine what measures should be taken to comply with the employer's or self-employed person's duties under the 'relevant statutory provisions' and Part II of the Fire Regulations. This covers the general duties in the HSW Act and the requirements of Part II of the Fire Regulations and the more specific duties in the various acts and regulations (including these Regulations) associated with the HSW Act. Once the measures have been determined in this way, the duty to put them into effect will be defined in the statutory provisions. For example a risk assessment on machinery would be undertaken under these Regulations, but the Provision and Use of Work Equipment Regulations (PUWER 1998)[9] determine what precautions must be carried out. A risk assessment carried out by a self-employed person in circumstances where he or she does not employ others does not have to take into account duties arising under Part II of the Fire Regulations.

Suitable and sufficient

13   A suitable and sufficient risk assessment should be made. 'Suitable and sufficient' is not defined in the Regulations. In practice it means the risk assessment should do the following:

(a)   The risk assessment should identify the risks arising from or in connection with work. The level of detail in a risk assessment should be proportionate to the risk. Once the risks are assessed and taken into account, insignificant risks can usually be ignored, as can risks arising from routine activities associated with life in general, unless the work activity compounds or significantly alters those risks. The level of risk arising from the work activity should determine the degree of sophistication of the risk assessment.

   (i)   For small businesses presenting few or simple hazards a suitable and sufficient risk assessment can be a very straightforward process based on informed judgement and reference to appropriate guidance. Where the hazards and

[9]S.I. 1998/2306.

risks are obvious, they can be addressed directly. No complicated processes or skills will be required.

(ii) In many intermediate cases the risk assessment will need to be more sophisticated. There may be some areas of the assessment for which specialist advice is required; for example risks which require specialist knowledge such as a particularly complex process or technique, or risks which need specialist analytical techniques such as being able to measure air quality and to assess its impact. Whenever specialist advisers are used, employers should ensure that the advisers have sufficient understanding of the particular work activity they are advising on, this will often require effective involvement of everyone concerned - employer, employees and specialist.

(iii) Large and hazardous sites will require the most developed and sophisticated risk assessments, particularly where there are complex or novel processes. In the case of certain manufacturing sites who use or store bulk hazardous substances, large scale mineral extraction or nuclear plant, the risk assessment will be a significant part of the safety case or report which is legally required and may incorporate such techniques as quantified risk assessment. A number of other statutory requirements exist (eg the Control of Major Accident Hazards (COMAH), and Nuclear Installations licensing arrangements) which include more specific and detailed arrangements for risk assessment.

(iv) Risk assessments must also consider all those who might be affected by the undertaking, whether they are workers or others such as members of the public. For example, the risk assessment produced by a railway company will *inter alia*, have to consider the hazards and risks which arise from the operation and maintenance of rail vehicles and train services and which might adversely affect workers (their own employees and others), passengers and any member of the public who could foreseeably be affected (eg level crossing users).

(b) Employers and the self-employed are expected to take reasonable steps to help themselves identify risks, eg by looking at appropriate sources of information, such as relevant legislation, appropriate guidance, supplier manuals and manufacturers' instructions and reading trade press, or seeking advice from competent sources. They should also look at and use relevant examples of good practice from within their industry. The risk assessment should include only what an employer or self-employed person could reasonably be expected to know; they would not be expected to anticipate risks that were not foreseeable;

(c) The risk assessment should be appropriate to the nature of the work and should identify the period of time for which it is likely to remain valid. This will enable management to recognise when short-term control measures need to be reviewed and modified, and to put in place medium and long-term controls where these are necessary.

14   For activities where the nature of the work may change fairly frequently or the workplace itself changes and develops (such as a construction site), or where workers move from site to site, the risk assessment might have to concentrate more on the broad range of risks that can be foreseen. When other less common risks arise, detailed planning and employee training will be needed to take account of those risks and enable them to be controlled.

Risk assessment in practice

15   There are no fixed rules about how a risk assessment should be carried out; indeed it will depend on the nature of the work or business and the types of hazards and risks. Paragraph 18 does, however, set out the general principles that should be followed. The risk assessment process needs to be practical and take account of the views of employees and their safety representatives who will have practical knowledge to contribute. It should involve management, whether or not advisers or consultants assist with the detail. Employers should ensure that those involved take all reasonable care in carrying out the risk assessment. For further guidance see HSE's publication *Five steps to risk assessment* (see References and further reading section).

16   Where employees of different employers work in the same workplace, their respective employers may have to co-operate to produce an overall risk assessment. Detailed requirements on co-operation and co-ordination are covered by Regulation 11.

17   In some cases employers may make a first rough assessment, to eliminate from consideration those risks on which no further action is needed. This should also show where a fuller assessment is needed, if appropriate, using more sophisticated techniques. Employers who control a number of similar workplaces containing similar activities may produce a 'model' risk assessment reflecting the core hazards and risks associated with these activities. 'Model' assessments may also be developed by trade associations, employers' bodies or other organisations concerned with a particular activity. Such 'model' assessments may be applied by employers or managers at each workplace, but only if they:

(a)   satisfy themselves that the 'model' assessment is appropriate to their type of work; and

(b)   adapt the 'model' to the detail of their own actual work situations, including any extension necessary to cover hazards and risks not referred to in the 'model'.

18   A risk assessment should:

(a)   ensure the significant risks and hazards are addressed;

(b)   ensure all aspects of the work activity are reviewed, including routine and non-routine activities. The assessment should cover all parts of the work activity, including those that are not under the immediate supervision of the employer, such as employees working off site as contractors, workers from one organisation temporarily working for another organisation, self-employed people, homeworkers and mobile employees. Details of where to find additional guidance on homeworkers and volunteers is given in the References and further reading section. Where workers visit members of the public in the home, eg nurses, employers should consider any risks arising from potential dangers;

(c)   take account of the non-routine operations, eg maintenance, cleaning operations, loading and unloading of vehicles, changes in production cycles, emergency response arrangements;

(d)   take account of the management of incidents such as interruptions to the work activity, which frequently cause accidents, and consider what procedures should be followed to mitigate the effects of the incident;

(e)   be systematic in identifying hazards and looking at risks, whether one risk assessment covers the whole activity or the assessment is divided up. For example, it may be necessary to look at activities in groups such as machinery, transport, substances, electrical etc, or to divide the work site on a geographical basis. In other cases, an operation by operation approach may be needed, dealing with materials in production, dispatch, offices etc. The employer or self-employed person should always adopt a structured approach to risk assessment to ensure all significant risks or hazards are addressed. Whichever method is chosen, it should reflect the skills and abilities of the individuals carrying out that aspect of the assessment;

(f)   take account of the way in which work is organised, and the effects this can have on health;

(g)   take account of risks to the public;

(h)   take account of the need to cover fire risks. The guide *Fire safety: An employer's guide* tells you how to comply with the law relating to fire issues and how to carry out a fire risk assessment (see References and further reading at the back of this document).

Identifying the hazards

19   First, identify what the hazards are.

20   If there are specific acts or regulations to be complied with, these may help to identify the hazards. Some regulations require the assessment of particular risks or types of risks. If these particular risks are present, they must all be addressed in a risk assessment process for the purpose of these Regulations.

Identifying who might be harmed and how

21   Identify people who might be harmed by the hazard, including employees, other workers in the workplace and members of the public. Do not forget office staff, night cleaners, maintenance staff, security guards, visitors and members of the public. You should identify groups of workers who might be particularly at risk, such as young or inexperienced workers, new and expectant mothers, night workers, homeworkers, those who work alone and disabled staff.

Evaluating the risks from the identified hazards

22   You need to evaluate the risks from the identified hazards. Of course, if there are no hazards, there are no risks. Where risks are

already controlled in some way, the effectiveness of those controls needs to be considered when assessing the extent of risk which remains. You also need to:

(a) observe the actual practice; this may differ from the works manual, and the employees concerned or their safety representatives should be consulted;

(b) address what actually happens in the workplace or during the work activity; and

(c) take account of existing preventive or precautionary measures; if existing measures are not adequate, ask yourself what more should be done to reduce risk sufficiently.

Recording

23   All employers and self-employed people are required to make a risk assessment. The regulation also provides that employers with five or more employees must record the significant findings of their risk assessment. This record should represent an effective statement of hazards and risks which then leads management to take the relevant actions to protect health and safety. The record should be retrievable for use by management in reviews and for safety representatives or other employee representatives and visiting inspectors. Where appropriate, it should be linked to other health and safety records or documents such as the record of health and safety arrangements required by regulation 5 and the written health and safety policy statement required by section 2(3) of the HSW Act. It may be possible to combine these documents into one health and safety management document.

24   This record may be in writing or recorded by other means (eg electronically) as long as it is retrievable and remains retrievable even when, for example, the technology of electronic recording changes. The record will often refer to other documents and records describing procedures and safeguards.

25   The significant findings should include:

(a) a record of the preventive and protective measures in place to control the risks;

(b) what further action, if any, needs to be taken to reduce risk sufficiently;

(c) proof that a suitable and sufficient assessment has been made. In many cases, employers (and the self-employed) will also need to record sufficient detail of the assessment itself, so that they can demonstrate (eg to an inspector or to safety representatives or other employee representatives) that they have carried out a suitable and sufficient assessment. This record of the significant findings will also form a basis for a revision of the assessment.

Review and revision

26   The regulation requires employers and the self-employed to review and, if necessary, modify their risk assessments, since assessment should not be a once-and-for-all activity. HSE's guide

Successful health and safety management (see References and further reading section) provides sound guidance on good practice. The following sub-paragraphs identify particular examples of review and revision.

(a)   As the nature of work changes, the appreciation of hazards and risks may develop. Monitoring under the arrangements required by regulation 5 may reveal near misses or defects in plant or equipment. The risk assessment may no longer be valid because of, for example, the results of health surveillance, or a confirmed case of occupationally induced disease. Adverse events such as an accident, ill health or dangerous occurrence may take place even if a suitable and sufficient risk assessment has been made and appropriate preventive and protective measures taken. Such events should be a trigger for reviewing the original assessment.

(b)   The employer or self-employed person needs to review the risk assessment if developments suggest that it may no longer be valid (or can be improved). In most cases, it is prudent to plan to review risk assessments at regular intervals. The time between reviews is dependent on the nature of the risks and the degree of change likely in the work activity. Such reviews should form part of standard management practice.

Assessment under other regulations

27   Other regulations also contain requirements for risk assessment specific to the hazards and risks they cover. Where an employer is assessing a work situation or activity for the first time, an assessment is particularly useful to identify where a more detailed risk assessment is needed to fulfil the requirements of other regulations.

28   An assessment made for the purpose of other regulations will partly cover the obligation to make assessments under these regulations. Where employers have already carried out assessments under other regulations, they need not repeat those assessments as long as they remain valid; but they do need to ensure that they cover all significant risks.

3

Principles of prevention to be applied

Where an employer implements any preventive and protective measures he shall do so on the basis of the principles specified in Schedule 1 to these Regulations.

29   Employers and the self-employed need to introduce preventive and protective measures to control the risks identified by the risk assessment in order to comply with the relevant legislation. A set of principles to be followed in identifying the appropriate measures are set out in Schedule 1 to the Regulations and are described below. Employers and the self-employed should use these to direct their approach to identifying and implementing the necessary measures.

30   In deciding which preventive and protective measures to take, employers and self-employed people should apply the following principles of prevention:

(a)   if possible avoid a risk altogether, eg do the work in a different way, taking care not to introduce new hazards;

(b)   evaluate risks that cannot be avoided by carrying out a risk assessment;

(c)   combat risks at source, rather than taking palliative measures. So, if the steps are slippery, treating or replacing them is better than displaying a warning sign;

(d)   adapt work to the requirements of the individual (consulting those who will be affected when designing workplaces, selecting work and personal protective equipment and drawing up working and safety procedures and methods of production). Aim to alleviate monotonous work and paced working at a predetermined rate, and increase the control individuals have over work they are responsible for;

(e)   take advantage of technological and technical progress, which often offers opportunities for improving working methods and making them safer;

(f)   implement risk prevention measures to form part of a coherent policy and approach. This will progressively reduce those risks that cannot be prevented or avoided altogether, and will take account of the way work is organised, the working conditions, the environment and any relevant social factors. Health and safety policy statements required under section 2(3) of the HSW Act should be prepared and applied by reference to these principles;

(g)   give priority to those measures which protect the whole workplace and everyone who works there, and so give the greatest benefit (ie give collective protective measures priority over individual measures);

(h)   ensure that workers, whether employees or self-employed, understand what they must do;

(i)   the existence of a positive health and safety culture should exist within an organisation. That means the avoidance, prevention and reduction of risks at work must be accepted as part of the organisation's approach and attitude to all its activities. It should be recognised at all levels of the organisation, from junior to senior management.

31   These are general principles rather than individual prescriptive requirements. They should, however, be applied wherever it is reasonable to do so. Experience suggests that, in the majority of cases, adopting good practice will be enough to ensure risks are reduced sufficiently. Authoritative sources of good practice are prescriptive legislation, Approved Codes of Practice and guidance produced by Government and HSE inspectors. Other sources include standards produced by standard-making organisations and guidance agreed by a body representing an industrial or occupational sector, provided the guidance has gained general acceptance. Where established industry practices result in high levels of health and safety, risk assessment should not be used to justify reducing current control measures.

Health and safety arrangements

(1) Every employer shall make and give effect to such arrangements as are appropriate, having regard to the nature of his activities and the size of his undertaking, for the effective planning, organisation, control, monitoring and review of the preventive and protective measures.

(2) Where the employer employs five or more employees, he shall record the arrangements referred to in paragraph (1).

32   This regulation requires employers to have arrangements in place to cover health and safety. Effective management of health and safety will depend, amongst other things, on a suitable and sufficient risk assessment being carried out and the findings being used effectively. The health and safety arrangements can be integrated into the management system for all other aspects of the organisation's activities. The management system adopted will need to reflect the complexity of the organisation's activities and working environment. Where the work process is straightforward and the risks generated are relatively simple to control, then very straightforward management systems may be appropriate. For large complicated organisations more complex systems may be appropriate. Although the principles of the management arrangements are the same irrespective of the size of an organisation. The key elements of such effective systems can be found in *Successful health and safety management* (see References and further reading section) or the British Standard for health and safety management systems BS8800. A successful health and safety management system will include all the following elements.

Planning

33   Employers should set up an effective health and safety management system to implement their health and safety policy which is proportionate to the hazards and risks. Adequate planning includes:

(a)   adopting a systematic approach to the completion of a risk assessment. Risk assessment methods should be used to decide on priorities and to set objectives for eliminating hazards and reducing risks. This should include a programme, with deadlines for the completion of the risk assessment process, together with suitable deadlines for the design and implementation of the preventive and protective measures which are necessary;

(b)   selecting appropriate methods of risk control to minimise risks;

(c)   establishing priorities and developing performance standards both for the completion of the risk assessment(s) and the implementation of preventive and protective measures, which at each stage minimises the risk of harm to people. Wherever possible, risks are eliminated through selection and design of facilities, equipment and processes.

Organisation

34   This includes:

(a)   involving employees and their representatives in carrying out risk assessments, deciding on preventive and protective measures and implementing those requirements in the workplace. This may be achieved by the use of formal health and safety committees where they exist, and by the use of teamworking, where employees are involved in deciding on the appropriate preventive and protective measures and written procedures etc;

(b) establishing effective means of communication and consultation in which a positive approach to health and safety is visible and clear. The employer should have adequate health and safety information and make sure it is communicated to employees and their representatives, so informed decisions can be made about the choice of preventive and protective measures. Effective communication will ensure that employees are provided with sufficient information so that control measures can be implemented effectively;

(c) securing competence by the provision of adequate information, instruction and training and its evaluation, particularly for those who carry out risk assessments and make decisions about preventive and protective measures. Where necessary this will need to be supported by the provision of adequate health and safety assistance or advice.

Control

35 Establishing control includes:

(a) clarifying health and safety responsibilities and ensuring that the activities of everyone are well co-ordinated;

(b) ensuring everyone with responsibilities understands clearly what they have to do to discharge their responsibilities, and ensure they have the time and resources to discharge them effectively;

(c) setting standards to judge the performance of those with responsibilities and ensure they meet them. It is important to reward good performance as well as to take action to improve poor performance; and

(d) ensuring adequate and appropriate supervision, particularly for those who are learning and who are new to a job.

Monitoring

36 Employers should measure what they are doing to implement their health and safety policy, to assess how effectively they are controlling risks, and how well they are developing a positive health and safety culture. Monitoring includes:

(a) having a plan and making adequate routine inspections and checks to ensure that preventive and protective measures are in place and effective. Active monitoring reveals how effectively the health and safety management system is functioning;

(b) adequately investigating the immediate and underlying causes of incidents and accidents to ensure that remedial action is taken, lessons are learnt and longer term objectives are introduced.

37 In both cases it may be appropriate to record and analyse the

results of monitoring activity, to identify any underlying themes or trends which may not be apparent from looking at events in isolation.

Review

38   Review involves:

(a)   establishing priorities for necessary remedial action that were discovered as a result of monitoring to ensure that suitable action is taken in good time and is completed;

(b)   periodically reviewing the whole of the health and safety management system including the elements of planning, organisation, control and monitoring to ensure that the whole system remains effective.

39   Consulting employees or their representatives about matters to do with their health and safety is good management practice, as well as being a requirement under health and safety law. Employees are a valuable source of information and can provide feedback about the effectiveness of health and safety management arrangements and control measures. Where safety representatives exist, they can act as an effective channel for employees' views.

40   Safety representatives' experience of workplace conditions and their commitment to health and safety means they often identify potential problems, allowing the employer to take prompt action. They can also have an important part to play in explaining safety measures to the workforce and gaining commitment.

Health surveillance

Every employer shall ensure that his employees are provided with such health surveillance as is appropriate having regard to the risks to their health and safety which are identified by the assessment.

41   **The risk assessment will identify circumstances in which health surveillance is required by specific health and safety regulations eg COSHH. Health surveillance should also be introduced where the assessment shows the following criteria to apply:**

(a)   **there is an identifiable disease or adverse health condition related to the work concerned; and**

(b)   **valid techniques are available to detect indications of the disease or condition; and**

(c)   **there is a reasonable likelihood that the disease or condition may occur under the particular conditions of work; and**

(d)   **surveillance is likely to further the protection of the health and safety of the employees to be covered.**

42   **Those employees concerned and their safety or other representatives should be given an explanation of, and opportunity to comment on, the nature and proposed frequency of such health surveillance procedures and should have access to an appropriately**

qualified practitioner for advice on surveillance.

43   The appropriate level, frequency and procedure of health surveillance should be determined by a competent person acting within the limits of their training and experience. This could be determined on the basis of suitable general guidance (eg regarding skin inspection for dermal effects) but in certain circumstances this may require the assistance of a qualified medical practitioner. The minimum requirement for health surveillance is keeping a health record. Once it is decided that health surveillance is appropriate, it should be maintained throughout an employee's employment unless the risk to which the worker is exposed and associated health effects are rare and short term.

44   Where appropriate, health surveillance may also involve one or more health surveillance procedures depending on suitability in the circumstances (a non-exhaustive list of examples of diseases is included in the footnote for guidance).[10] Such procedures can include:

(a)   inspection of readily detectable conditions by a responsible person acting within the limits of their training and experience;

(b)   enquiries about symptoms, inspection and examination by a qualified person such as an Occupational Health Nurse;

(c)   medical surveillance, which may include clinical examination and measurement of physiological or psychological effects by an appropriately qualified person;

(d)   biological effect monitoring, ie the measurement and assessment of early biological effects such as diminished lung function in exposed workers; and

(e)   biological monitoring, ie the measurement and assessment of workplace agents or their metabolites either in tissues, secreta, excreta, expired air or any combination of these in exposed workers.

45   The primary benefit, and therefore objective of health surveillance should be to detect adverse health effects at an early stage, thereby enabling further harm to be prevented. The results of health surveillance can provide a means of:

(a)   checking the effectiveness of control measures;

(b)   providing feedback on the accuracy of the risk assessment; and

(c)   identifying and protecting individuals at increased risk because of the nature of their work.

[10]If the worker is exposed to noise or hand-arm vibrations, health surveillance may be needed under these regulations. If the worker is exposed to hazardous substances such as chemicals, solvents, fumes, dusts, gases and vapours, aerosols, biological agents (micro-organisms), health surveillance may be needed under COSHH. If the worker is exposed to asbestos, lead, work in compressed air, medical examinations may be needed under specific regulations.

Health and safety assistance

(1)   Every employer shall, subject to paragraphs (6) and (7), appoint one or more competent persons to assist him in undertaking the measures he needs to take to comply with the requirements and prohibitions imposed upon him by or under the relevant statutory provisions and by Part II of the Fire Precautions (Workplace) Regulations 1997.

(2)   Where an employer appoints persons in accordance with paragraph (1), he shall make arrangements for ensuring adequate co-operation between them.

(3)   The employer shall ensure that the number of persons appointed under paragraph (1), the time available for them to fulfil their functions and the means at their disposal are adequate having regard to the size of his undertaking, the risks to which his employees are exposed and the distribution of those risks throughout the undertaking.

(4)   The employer shall ensure that-

(a)   any person appointed by him in accordance with paragraph (1) who is not in his employment-

(i)   is informed of the factors known by him to affect, or suspected by him of affecting, the health and safety of any other person who may be affected by the conduct of his undertaking, and

(ii)   has access to the information referred to in regulation 10; and

(b)   any person appointed by him in accordance with paragraph (1) is given such information about any person working in his undertaking who is-

(i)   employed by him under a fixed-term contract of employment, or

(ii)   employed in an employment business,

as is necessary to enable that person properly to carry out the function specified in that paragraph.

(5)   A person shall be regarded as competent for the purposes of paragraphs (1) and (8) where he has sufficient training and experience or knowledge and other qualities to enable him properly to assist in undertaking the measures referred to in paragraph (1).

(6)   Paragraph (1) shall not apply to a self-employed employer who is not in partnership with any other person where he has sufficient training and experience or knowledge and other qualities properly to undertake the measures referred to in that paragraph himself.

(7)   Paragraph (1) shall not apply to individuals who are employers and who are together carrying on business in partnership where at least one of the individuals concerned has sufficient training and experience or knowledge and other qualities-

(a)   properly to undertake the measures he needs to take to comply with the requirements and prohibitions imposed upon him by or under the relevant statutory provisions; and

(b)   properly to assist his fellow partners in undertaking the measures they need to take to comply with the requirements and prohibitions imposed upon them by or under the relevant statutory provisions.

(8)   Where there is a competent person in the employer's employment, that person shall be appointed for the purposes of paragraph (1) in preference to a competent person not in his employment.

46 **Employers are solely responsible for ensuring that those they appoint to assist them with health and safety measures are competent to carry out the tasks they are assigned and are given adequate information and support. In making decisions on who to appoint, employers themselves need to know and understand the work involved, the principles of risk assessment and prevention, and current legislation and health and safety standards. Employers should ensure that anyone they appoint is capable of applying the above to whatever task they are assigned.**

47 **Employers must have access to competent help in applying the provisions of health and safety law, including these Regulations. In particular they need competent help in devising and applying protective measures, unless they are competent to undertake the measures without assistance. Appointment of competent people for this purpose should be included among the health and safety arrangements recorded under regulation 5(2). Employers are required by the Safety Representatives and Safety Committees Regulations 1977 to consult safety representatives in good time on arrangements for the appointment of competent assistance.**

48 When seeking competent assistance employers should look to appoint one or more of their employees, with the necessary means, or themselves, to provide the health and safety assistance required. If there is no relevant competent worker in the organisation or the level of competence is insufficient to assist the employer in complying with health and safety law, the employer should enlist an external service or person. In some circumstances a combination of internal and external competence might be appropriate, recognising the limitations of the internal competence. Some regulations contain specific requirements for obtaining advice from competent people to assist in complying with legal duties. For example the Ionising Radiation Regulations requires the appointment of a radiation protection adviser in many circumstances, where work involves ionising radiations.

49 Employers who appoint doctors, nurses or other health professionals to advise them of the effects of work on employee health, or to carry out certain procedures, for example health surveillance, should first check that such providers can offer evidence of a sufficient level of expertise or training in occupational health. Registers of competent practitioners are maintained by several professional bodies, and are often valuable.

50 The appointment of such health and safety assistants or advisers does not absolve the employer from responsibilities for health and safety under the HSW Act and other relevant statutory provisions and under Part II of the Fire Regulations. It can only give added assurance that these responsibilities will be discharged adequately. Where external services are employed, they will usually be appointed in an advisory capacity only.

51 Competence in the sense it is used in these Regulations does not necessarily depend on the possession of particular skills or qualifications. Simple situations may require only the following:

(a) an understanding of relevant current best practice;

(b) an awareness of the limitations of one's own experience and knowledge; and

(c) the willingness and ability to supplement existing experience and knowledge, when necessary by obtaining external help and advice.

52   More complicated situations will require the competent assistant to have a higher level of knowledge and experience. More complex or highly technical situations will call for specific applied knowledge and skills which can be offered by appropriately qualified specialists. Employers are advised to check the appropriate health and safety qualifications (some of which may be competence-based and/or industry specific), or membership of a professional body or similar organisation (at an appropriate level and in an appropriate part of health and safety) to satisfy themselves that the assistant they appoint has a sufficiently high level of competence. Competence-based qualifications accredited by the Qualifications and Curriculum Authority and the Scottish Qualifications Authority may also provide a guide.

Regulation 8

Procedures for serious and imminent danger and for danger areas

(1)   Every employer shall-

(a)   establish and where necessary give effect to appropriate procedures to be followed in the event of serious and imminent danger to persons at work in his undertaking;

(b)   nominate a sufficient number of competent persons to implement those procedures in so far as they relate to the evacuation from premises of persons at work in his undertaking; and

(c)   ensure that none of his employees has access to any area occupied by him to which it is necessary to restrict access on grounds of health and safety unless the employee concerned has received adequate health and safety instruction.

(2)   Without prejudice to the generality of paragraph (1)(a), the procedures referred to in that sub-paragraph shall-

(a)   so far as is practicable, require any persons at work who are exposed to serious and imminent danger to be informed of the nature of the hazard and of the steps taken or to be taken to protect them from it;

(b)   enable the persons concerned (if necessary by taking appropriate steps in the absence of guidance or instruction and in the light of their knowledge and the technical means at their disposal) to stop work and immediately proceed to a place of safety in the event of their being exposed to serious, imminent and unavoidable danger; and

(c)   save in exceptional cases for reasons duly substantiated (which cases and reasons shall be specified in those procedures), require the persons concerned to be prevented from resuming work in any situation where there is still a serious and imminent danger.

(3)   A person shall be regarded as competent for the purposes of paragraph (1)(b) where he has sufficient training and experience or knowledge and other qualities to enable him properly to implement the evacuation procedures referred to in that sub-paragraph.

Contacts with external services

Every employer shall ensure that any necessary contacts with external services are arranged, particularly as regards first-aid, emergency medical care and rescue work.

53 Employers should establish procedures for any worker to follow if situations presenting serious and imminent danger were to arise, eg a fire, or for the police and emergency services an outbreak of public disorder. The procedures should set out:

(a) the nature of the risk (eg a fire in certain parts of a building where substances might be involved), and how to respond to it;

(b) additional procedures needed to cover risks beyond those posed by fire and bombs. These procedures should be geared, as far as is practicable, to the nature of the serious and imminent danger that those risks might pose;

(c) the additional responsibilities of any employees, or groups of employees, who may have specific tasks to perform in the event of emergencies (eg to shut down a plant that might otherwise compound the danger); or who have had training so that they can seek to bring an emergency event under control. Police officers, fire-fighters and other emergency service workers, for example, may sometimes need to work in circumstances of serious or imminent danger in order to fulfill their commitment to the public service. The procedures should reflect these responsibilities, and the time delay before such workers can move to a place of safety. Appropriate preventive and protective measures should be in place for these employees;

(d) the role, responsibilities and authority of the competent people nominated to implement the detailed actions. The procedures should also ensure that employees know who the relevant competent people are and understand their role;

(e) any requirements laid on employers by health and safety regulations which cover some specific emergency situations;

(f) details of when and how the procedures are to be activated so that employees can proceed in good time to a place of safety. Procedures should cater for the fact that emergency events can occur and develop rapidly, thus requiring employees to act without waiting for further guidance. It may be necessary to commence evacuation while attempts to control an emergency (eg a process in danger of running out of control) are still under way, in case those attempts fail.

54 Emergency procedures should normally be written down as required by regulation 5(2), clearly setting out the limits of actions to be taken by employees. Information on the procedures should be made available to all employees (under regulation 10), to any external health and safety personnel appointed under regulation 7(1), and where necessary to other workers and/or their employers under regulation 12. Induction training, carried out under regulation 13, should cover emergency procedures and should familiarise employees with those procedures.

55   **Work should not be resumed after an emergency if a serious danger remains. If there are any doubts, expert assistance should be sought, eg from the emergency services and others. There may, for certain groups of workers, be exceptional circumstances when re-entry to areas of serious danger may be deemed necessary, eg police officers, fire-fighters and other emergency service workers, where, for example, human life is at risk. When such exceptional circumstances can be anticipated, the procedures should set out the special protective measures to be taken (and the pre-training required) and the steps to be taken for authorisation of such actions.**

56   The procedure for any worker to follow in serious and imminent danger, has to be clearly explained by the employer. Employees and others at work need to know when they should stop work and how they should move to a place of safety. In some cases this will require full evacuation of the workplace; in others it might mean some or all of the workforce moving to a safer part of the workplace.

57   The risk assessment should identify the foreseeable events that need to be covered by these procedures. For some employers, fire (and possibly bomb) risks will be the only ones that need to be covered. For others, additional risks will be identified.

58   Where different employers (or self-employed people) share a workplace, their separate emergency procedures will need to take account of everyone in the workplace, and as far as is appropriate the procedures should be co-ordinated. Detailed requirements on co-operation and co-ordination are covered by regulation 11.

Danger areas

59   A danger area is a work environment which must be entered by an employee where the level of risk is unacceptable without taking special precaution. Such areas are not necessarily static in that minor alterations or an emergency may convert a normal working environment into a danger area. The hazard involved need not occupy the whole area, as in the case of a toxic gas, but can be localised, eg where there is a risk of an employee coming into contact with bare live electrical conductors. The area must be restricted to prevent inadvertent access.

60   This regulation does not specify the precautions to take to ensure safe working in the danger area - this is covered by other legislation. However, once the employer has established suitable precautions the relevant employees must receive adequate instruction and training in those precautions before entering any such danger area.

Contacts with external services

61   The employer should ensure that appropriate external contacts are in place to make sure there are effective provisions for first aid, emergency medical care and rescue work, for incidents and accidents which may require urgent action, and/or medical attention beyond the capabilities of on-site personnel. This may only mean making sure that employees know the necessary telephone numbers and, where there is a significant risk, that they are able to contact any help they need. This requirement does not in any way reduce employers' duty to prevent accidents as the first priority.

62   Where a number of employers share a workplace and their employees face the same risks, it would be possible for one employer to arrange contacts

on behalf of themselves and the other employers. In these circumstances it would be for the other employers to ensure that the contacts had been made. In hazardous or complex workplaces, employers should designate appropriate staff to routinely contact the emergency services to give them sufficient knowledge of the risks they need to take appropriate action in emergencies, including those likely to happen outside normal working hours. This will help these services in planning for providing first aid, emergency medical care and rescue work, and to take account of risks to everyone involved, including rescuers. Contacts and arrangements with external services should be recorded, and should be reviewed and revised as necessary, in the light of changes to staff, processes and plant, and revisions to health and safety procedures.

Regulation 10

Regulation

Information for employees

(1) Every employer shall provide his employees with comprehensible and relevant information on-

    (a)   the risks to their health and safety identified by the assessment;

    (b)   the preventive and protective measures;

    (c)   the procedures referred to in regulation 8(1)(a) and the measures referred to in regulation 4(2)(a) of the Fire Precautions (Workplace) Regulations 1997;

    (d)   the identity of those persons nominated by him in accordance with regulation 8(1)(b) and regulation 4(2)(b) of the Fire Precautions (Workplace) Regulations 1997; and

    (e)   the risks notified to him in accordance with regulation 11(1)(c).

(2) Every employer shall, before employing a child, provide a parent of the child with comprehensible and relevant information on-

    (a)   the risks to his health and safety identified by the assessment;

    (b)   the preventive and protective measures; and

    (c)   the risks notified to him in accordance with regulation 11(1)(c).

(3) The reference in paragraph (2) to a parent of the child includes-

    (a)   in England and Wales, a person who has parental responsibility, within the meaning of section 3 of the Children Act 1989[(a)], for him; and

    (b)   in Scotland, a person who has parental rights, within the meaning of section 8 of the Law Reform (Parent and Child) (Scotland)) Act 1986[(b)] for him.

[(a)] *1989 c.41.*
[(b)] *1986 c.9.*

Guidance

9

10

63   The risk assessment will help identify information which has to be provided to employees under specific regulations, as well as any further information relevant to risks to employees' health and safety. Relevant information on risks and on preventive and protective measures will be limited to what employees need to know to ensure their own health and safety and not to put others at risk. This regulation also requires information to be provided on the emergency arrangements established under regulation 8, including the identity of staff nominated to help if there is an evacuation.

64   The information provided should be pitched appropriately, given the level of training, knowledge and experience of the employee. It should be provided in a form which takes account of any language difficulties or disabilities. Information can be provided in whatever form is most suitable in the circumstances, as long as it can be understood by everyone. For employees with little or no understanding of English, or who cannot read English, employers may need to make special arrangements. These could include providing translation, using interpreters, or replacing written notices with clearly understood symbols or diagrams.

65   This regulation applies to all employees, including trainees and those on fixed-duration contracts. Additional information for employees on fixed-duration contracts is contained in regulation 15. Specific requirements relate to the provision of information to safety representatives, and enabling full and effective consultation of employees.[11]

66   While a child (below minimum school leaving age) is at work, the requirements to provide information are the same as for other employees. There is, however, an extra requirement on the employer to provide the parents or guardians of children at work (including those on work experience) with information on the key findings of the risk assessment and the control measures taken, before the child starts work. This information can be provided in any appropriate form, including verbally or directly to the parents or guardians, or in the case of work experience, via an organisation such as the school, the work experience agency, or, if agreed with the parents, via the child him or herself, as long as this is considered a reliable method.

Co-operation and co-ordination

(1) Where two or more employers share a workplace (whether on a temporary or a permanent basis) each such employer shall-

> *(a)   co-operate with the other employers concerned so far as is necessary to enable them to comply with the requirements and prohibitions imposed upon them by or under the relevant statutory provisions and by Part II of the Fire Precautions (Workplace) Regulations 1997;*

> *(b)   (taking into account the nature of his activities) take all reasonable steps to co-ordinate the measures he takes to comply with the requirements and prohibitions imposed upon him by or under the relevant statutory provisions and by Part II of the Fire Precautions (Workplace) Regulations 1997 with the measures the other employers concerned are taking to comply with the requirements and prohibitions imposed upon them by that legislation; and*

> *(c)   take all reasonable steps to inform the other employers concerned of the*

[11]Safety Representatives and Safety Committees Regulations 1977 SI1977/500 and Health and Safety (Consultation with Employees) Regulations 1996 SI1996/1513.

risks to their employees' health and safety arising out of or in connection with the conduct by him of his undertaking.

(2)   Paragraph (1) (except in so far as it refers to Part II of the Fire Precautions (Workplace) Regulations 1997) shall apply to employers sharing a workplace with self-employed persons and to self-employed persons sharing a workplace with other self-employed persons as it applies to employers sharing a workplace with other employers; and the references in that paragraph to employers and the reference in the said paragraph to their employees shall be construed accordingly.

67   To meet the requirements of these Regulations, such as carrying out a risk assessment under regulation 3 and establishing procedures to follow serious and dangerous situations under regulation 8, it is necessary to cover the whole workplace to be fully effective. When the workplace is occupied by more than one employer, this will require some degree of co-ordination and co-operation. All employers and self-employed people involved should satisfy themselves that the arrangements adopted are adequate. Employers should ensure that all their employees, but especially the competent people appointed under regulations 7 and 8, are aware of and take full part in the arrangements. Specific co-ordination arrangements may be required by other regulations.

68   Where a particular employer controls the workplace, others should assist the controlling employer in assessing the shared risks and co-ordinating any necessary measures. In many situations providing information may be sufficient. A controlling employer who has established site-wide arrangements will have to inform new employers or self-employed people of those arrangements so that they can integrate themselves into the co-operation and co-ordination procedures.

69   Where the activities of different employers and self-employed people interact, for example where they share premises or workplaces, they may need to co-operate with each other to make sure their respective obligations are met. This regulation does not extend to the relationship between a host employer and a contractor, which will be covered by regulation 12.

70   The duties to co-operate and co-ordinate measures relate to all statutory duties, except for Part II of the Fire Regulations, in the case of people who are self-employed and are not employers. Therefore, they concern all people who may be at risk, both on and off site, and not just where employers and self-employed people share workplaces all the time. They also include situations where an employer may not be physically present at the workplace.

Appointment of health and safety co-ordinator

71   Where there is no controlling employer, the employers and self-employed people present will need to agree any joint arrangements needed to meet the requirements of the Regulations, such as appointing a health and safety co-ordinator. This will be particularly useful in workplaces where management control is fragmented and employment is largely casual or short term (eg in construction). The Construction (Design and Management) Regulations 1994[12] require principal contractors to ensure co-operation between all contractors. In workplaces which are complex or contain significant hazards, the controlling employer or health and safety co-ordinator (on behalf of the employers etc present) may need to seek competent advice in making or assisting with the risk assessment and determining appropriate measures. Employers do not absolve themselves of their legal responsibilities by

[12]S.I. 1994/3140.

appointing such co-ordinators who provide competent advice.

Person in control

72   The person in control of a multi-occupancy workplace may not always be an employer of the people working in that workplace or be self-employed, but will still need to co-operate with those occupying the workplace under their control. For example, procedures for authorising or carrying out repairs and modifications will have to take account of the need for co-operation and exchanges of information. Co-operation is needed to effectively carry out the general duties placed on those people under section 4 of the HSW Act, as well as more specific duties under other Regulations (eg in offshore health and safety legislation or in relation to welfare facilities provided under the Workplace (Health, Safety and Welfare) Regulations 1992).[13]

73   People who control the premises and make arrangements to co-ordinate health and safety activities, particularly for emergencies, may help employers and self-employed people who participate in those arrangements to comply with regulation 11(1)(b).

74   This regulation does not apply to multi-occupancy buildings or sites, where each unit under the control of an individual tenant employer or self-employed person is regarded as a separate workplace. In some cases, however, the common parts of such multi-occupancy sites may be shared workplaces (eg a common reception area in an office building) or may be under the control of a person to whom section 4 of the HSW Act applies and suitable arrangements may need to be put in place for these areas.

Persons working in host employers' or self-employed persons' undertakings

(1)   Every employer and every self-employed person shall ensure that the employer of any employees from an outside undertaking who are working in his undertaking is provided with comprehensible information on-

> *(a)   the risks to those employees' health and safety arising out of or in connection with the conduct by that first-mentioned employer or by that self-employed person of his undertaking; and*

> *(b)   the measures taken by that first-mentioned employer or by that self-employed person in compliance with the requirements and prohibitions imposed upon him by or under the relevant statutory provisions and by Part II of the Fire Precautions (Workplace) Regulations 1997 in so far as the said requirements and prohibitions relate to those employees.*

(2)   Paragraph (1) (except in so far as it refers to Part II of the Fire Precautions (Workplace) Regulations 1997) shall apply to a self-employed person who is working in the undertaking of an employer or a self-employed person as it applies to employees from an outside undertaking who are working therein; and the reference in that paragraph to the employer of any employees from an outside undertaking who are working in the undertaking of an employer or a self-employed person and the references in the said paragraph to employees from an outside undertaking who are

[13]S.I. 1992/3004.

working in the undertaking of an employer or a self-employed person shall be construed accordingly.

(3) Every employer shall ensure that any person working in his undertaking who is not his employee and every self-employed person (not being an employer) shall ensure that any person working in his undertaking is provided with appropriate instructions and comprehensible information regarding any risks to that person's health and safety which arise out of the conduct by that employer or self-employed person of his undertaking.

(4) Every employer shall-

(a) ensure that the employer of any employees from an outside undertaking who are working in his undertaking is provided with sufficient information to enable that second-mentioned employer to identify any person nominated by that first mentioned employer in accordance with regulation 8(1)(b) to implement evacuation procedures as far as those employees are concerned; and

(b) take all reasonable steps to ensure that any employees from an outside undertaking who are working in his undertaking receive sufficient information to enable them to identify any person nominated by him in accordance with regulation 8(1)(b) to implement evacuation procedures as far as they are concerned.

(5) Paragraph (4) shall apply to a self-employed person who is working in an employer's undertaking as it applies to employees from an outside undertaking who are working therein; and the reference in that paragraph to the employer of any employees from an outside undertaking who are working in an employer's undertaking and the references in the said paragraph to employees from an outside undertaking who are working in an employer's undertaking shall be construed accordingly.

75   **The risk assessment carried out under regulation 3 will identify risks to people other than the host employers' employees. This will include other employers' employees and self-employed people working in that business. Employers and self-employed people need to ensure that comprehensive information on those risks, and the measures taken to control them is given to other employers and self-employed people. Further guidance can be found under regulation 10.**

76   **Host employers and self-employed people must ensure that people carrying out work on their premises receive relevant information. This may be done by either providing them with information directly or by ensuring that their employers provide them with the relevant information. If you rely on their employers to provide information to the visiting employees, then adequate checks should be carried out to ensure that the information is passed on. The information should be sufficient to allow the employer of the visiting employee to comply with their statutory duties, and should include the identity of people nominated by the host employer to help with an emergency evacuation under regulation 8.**

77   **Information may be provided through a written permit-to-work system. Where the visiting employees are specialists, brought in to do specialist tasks, the host employer's instructions need to be concerned with those risks which are peculiar to the activity and premises. The visiting employee may also introduce risks to the permanent workforce (eg from equipment or substances they may bring with them). Their**

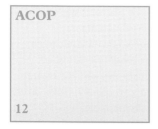
employers have a general duty under section 3 of the HSW Act to inform the host employer of such risks and to co-operate and co-ordinate with the host employer to the extent needed to control those risks.

78   The guidance on information for employees under regulation 10 applies equally to information provided under regulation 12.

79   This regulation applies where employees or self-employed people carry out work for an employer other than their own or of another self-employed person. This will include contractors' employees carrying out cleaning, repair, or maintenance work under a service contract; and employees in temporary employment businesses, hired to work under a host employer's control (additional requirements for information to employment businesses are under regulation 15). Safety representatives and other employee representatives are often used to ensure information is supplied to everyone who comes on site.

Regulation 13

Capabilities and training

(1)   Every employer shall, in entrusting tasks to his employees, take into account their capabilities as regards health and safety.

(2)   Every employer shall ensure that his employees are provided with adequate health and safety training-

(a)   on their being recruited into the employer's undertaking; and

(b)   on their being exposed to new or increased risks because of -

(i)   their being transferred or given a change of responsibilities within the employer's undertaking,

(ii)   the introduction of new work equipment into or a change respecting work equipment already in use within the employer's undertaking,

(iii)   the introduction of new technology into the employer's undertaking, or

(iv)   the introduction of a new system of work into or a change respecting a system of work already in use within the employer's undertaking.

(3)   The training referred to in paragraph (2) shall-

(a)   be repeated periodically where appropriate;

(b)   be adapted to take account of any new or changed risks to the health and safety of the employees concerned; and

(c)   take place during working hours.

80   When allocating work to employees, employers should ensure that the demands of the job do not exceed the employees' ability to carry out the work without risk to themselves or others. Employers should take account of the employees' capabilities and the level of their training, knowledge and experience. Managers should be aware of relevant legislation and should be competent to manage health and safety effectively. Employers should review their employees' capabilities to carry out their work, as necessary. If additional training, including refresher training, is needed, it should be provided.

81   Health and safety training should take place during working hours. If it is necessary to arrange training outside an employee's normal hours, this should be treated as an extension of time at work. Employees are not required to pay for their own training. Section 9 of the HSW Act prohibits employers from charging employees for anything they have to do or are required to do in respect of carrying out specific requirements of the relevant statutory provisions. The requirement to provide health and safety training is such a provision.

82   The risk assessment and subsequent reviews of the risk assessment will help determine the level of training and competence needed for each type of work. Competence is the ability to do the work required to the necessary standard. All employees, including senior management, should receive relevant training. This may need to include basic skills training, specific on-the-job training and training in health and safety or emergency procedures. There may be a need for further training eg about specific risks, required by other legislation. For those working towards National and Scottish Vocational Qualifications, the Employment National Training Organisation has designed stand-alone training units in health, safety and the environment. These vocational units are for people at work who are not health and safety professionals/specialists.

83   Training needs are likely to be greatest for new employees on recruitment. They should receive basic induction training on health and safety, including arrangements for first-aid, fire and evacuation. Particular attention should be given to the needs of young workers. The risk assessment should identify further specific training needs. In some cases, training may be required even though an employee already holds formal qualifications (eg for an update on new technology). Training and competence needs will have to be reviewed if the work activity a person is involved in or the working environment changes. This may include a change of department or the introduction of new equipment, processes or tasks.

84   An employee's competence will decline if skills are not used regularly (eg in emergency procedures, operating a particular item of equipment or carrying out a task). Training therefore needs to be repeated periodically to ensure continued competence. This will be particularly important for employees who occasionally deputise for others, home workers and mobile employees. Information from personal performance monitoring, health and safety checks, accident investigations and near-miss incidents can help to establish a suitable period for re-training. Employers are required by the Safety Representatives and Safety Committees Regulations 1997 to consult safety representatives in good time about the planning and organisation of health and safety training required for the employees they represent.

Employees' duties

(1) Every employee shall use any machinery, equipment, dangerous substance, transport equipment, means of production or safety device provided to him by his employer in accordance both with any training in the use of the equipment concerned which has been received by him and the instructions respecting that use which have been provided to him by the said employer in compliance with the requirements and prohibitions imposed upon that employer by or under the relevant statutory provisions.

(2) Every employee shall inform his employer or any other employee of that employer with specific responsibility for the health and safety of his fellow employees-

> *(a) of any work situation which a person with the first-mentioned employee's training and instruction would reasonably consider represented a serious and immediate danger to health and safety; and*

> *(b) of any matter which a person with the first-mentioned employee's training and instruction would reasonably consider represented a shortcoming in the employer's protection arrangements for health and safety,*

in so far as that situation or matter either affects the health and safety of that first mentioned employee or arises out of or in connection with his own activities at work, and has not previously been reported to his employer or to any other employee of that employer in accordance with this paragraph.

85   Employees' duties under section 7 of the HSW Act include co-operating with their employer to enable the employer to comply with statutory duties for health and safety. Under these Regulations, employers or those they appoint (eg under regulation 7) to assist them with health and safety matters need to be informed without delay of any work situation which might present a serious and imminent danger. Employees should also notify any shortcomings in the health and safety arrangements, even when no immediate danger exists, so that employers can take remedial action if needed.

86   The duties placed on employees do not reduce the responsibility of the employer to comply with duties under these Regulations and the other relevant statutory provisions. In particular, employers need to ensure that employees receive adequate instruction and training to enable them to comply with their duties.

87   Employees have a duty under section 7 of the HSW Act to take reasonable care for their own health and safety and that of others who may be affected by their actions or omissions at work. Therefore, employees must use all work items provided by their employer correctly, in accordance with their training and the instructions they received to use them safely.

Temporary workers

(1) Every employer shall provide any person whom he has employed under a fixed-term contract of employment with comprehensible information on-

> *(a) any special occupational qualifications or skills required to be held by that employee if he is to carry out his work safely; and*

> *(b) any health surveillance required to be provided to that employee by or*

under any of the relevant statutory provisions,

and shall provide the said information before the employee concerned commences his duties.

(2) Every employer and every self-employed person shall provide any person employed in an employment business who is to carry out work in his undertaking with comprehensible information on-

> *(a) any special occupational qualifications or skills required to be held by that employee if he is to carry out his work safely; and*

> *(b) health surveillance required to be provided to that employee by or under any of the relevant statutory provisions.*

(3) Every employer and every self-employed person shall ensure that every person carrying on an employment business whose employees are to carry out work in his undertaking is provided with comprehensible information on-

> *(a) any special occupational qualifications or skills required to be held by those employees if they are to carry out their work safely; and*

> *(b) the specific features of the jobs to be filled by those employees (in so far as those features are likely to affect their health and safety);*

and the person carrying on the employment business concerned shall ensure that the information so provided is given to the said employees.

15

88   This regulation supplements previous regulations requiring the provision of information with additional requirements on temporary workers (ie those employed on fixed-duration contracts and those employed in employment businesses, but working for a user company). The use of temporary workers needs to be notified to health and safety staff under regulation 7(4)(b), as necessary.

Fixed-duration contracts

89   Regulation 10 deals with the provision of information by employers to their employees. This includes those on fixed-duration contracts. Under regulation 15(1), employees on fixed-duration contracts also have to be informed of any special occupational qualifications or skills required to carry out the work safely and whether the job is subject to statutory health surveillance (the latter being a protective measure covered in general by regulation 10(1)(b)).

Employment businesses

90   Regulation 12(4) deals with the provision of information by a first employer to a second employer, whose employees are working on the premises. This includes employees of people who have an employment business. Under regulation 15(3), an employment business has to be informed of any special occupational qualifications or skills required to carry out the work safely and the specific features of the job which might affect health and safety (eg work at heights).

91   The person who has an employment business and the user employer both have duties to provide information to the employee. The person with the employment business has a duty under regulation 10 (as an employer) and a

15

duty under regulation 15(3) to ensure that the information provided by the user employer is given to the employee. The user employer has a duty under regulation 12(4) to check that information provided to an employer (including someone carrying on an employment business) is received by the employee. In addition, regulations 15(1) and (2) require that information on qualifications, skills and health surveillance are given directly to employees in an employment business.

92   These duties overlap to make sure the information needs of those working for, but not employed by, user employers are not overlooked. User employers and people carrying on employment businesses should therefore make suitable arrangements to satisfy themselves that information is provided. In most cases, it may be enough for user employees to provide information directly to employees. Those carrying on employment businesses will need to satisfy themselves that arrangements for this are adequate. However, basic information on job demands and risks should be supplied to the employment business at an early stage to help select those most suitable to carry out the work (in accordance with regulation 15(3)).

Self-employed

93   Self-employed people have similar duties under regulations 11(2), 12, 15(2) and 15(3) to inform employment businesses and the employees of employment businesses who carry out work on their premises. They may also need to agree arrangements with the employment businesses concerned. Self-employed workers hired through employment businesses are entitled to receive health and safety information from the employers or self-employed people for whom they carry out work under regulation 12(2). There is a full definition of how these Regulations apply to self-employed workers in paragraphs 4 and 5. It explains how people working under the control and direction of others but are treated as self-employed for other reasons such as tax and national insurance, are nevertheless treated as their employees for health and safety purposes.

15

Regulation 16

Risk assessment in respect of new or expectant mothers

(1)   Where -

(a)   the persons working in an undertaking include women of child-bearing age; and

(b)   the work is of a kind which could involve risk, by reason of her condition, to the health and safety of a new or expectant mother, or to that of her baby, from any processes or working conditions, or physical, biological or chemical agents, including those specified in Annexes I and II of Council Directive 92/85/EEC[(a)] on the introduction of measures to encourage improvements in the safety and health at work of pregnant workers and workers who have recently given birth or are breastfeeding,

the assessment required by regulation 3(1) shall also include an assessment of such risk.

(2)   Where, in the case of an individual employee, the taking of any other action the employer is required to take under the relevant statutory provisions would not avoid the risk referred to in paragraph (1) the employer shall, if it is reasonable to do so, and would avoid such risks, alter her working conditions or hours of work.

16

31

(3) If it is not reasonable to alter the working conditions or hours of work, or if it would not avoid such risk, the employer shall, subject to section 67 of the 1996 Act suspend the employee from work for so long as is necessary to avoid such risk.

(4) In paragraphs (1) to (3) references to risk, in relation to risk from any infectious or contagious disease, are references to a level of risk at work which is in addition to the level to which a new or expectant mother may be expected to be exposed outside the workplace.

(a)OJ No. L348, 28.11.92, p.1.

Regulation 17

Certificate from registered medical practitioner in respect of new or expectant mothers

1. Where-

(a) a new or expectant mother works at night; and

(b) a certificate from a registered medical practitioner or a registered midwife shows that it is necessary for her health or safety that she should not be at work for any period of such work identified in the certificate,

the employer shall, subject to section 67 of the 1996 Act, suspend her from work for so long as is necessary for her health or safety.

Regulation 18

Notification by new or expectant mothers

(1) Nothing in paragraph (2) or (3) of regulation 16 shall require the employer to take any action in relation to an employee until she has notified the employer in writing that she is pregnant, has given birth within the previous six months, or is breastfeeding.

(2) Nothing in paragraph (2) or (3) of regulation 16 or in regulation 17 shall require the employer to maintain action taken in relation to an employee-

(a) in a case-

(i) to which regulation 16(2) or (3) relates; and

(ii) where the employee has notified her employer that she is pregnant, where she has failed, within a reasonable time of being requested to do so in writing by her employer, to produce for the employer's inspection a certificate from a registered medical practitioner or a registered midwife showing that she is pregnant;

(b) once the employer knows that she is no longer a new or expectant mother; or

(c) if the employer cannot establish whether she remains a new or expectant mother.

32

94   Where the risk assessment identifies risks to new and expectant mothers and these risks cannot be avoided by the preventive and protective measures taken by an employer, the employer will need to:

(a)   alter her working conditions or hours of work if it is reasonable to do so and would avoid the risks or, if these conditions cannot be met;

(b)   identify and offer her suitable alternative work that is available, and if that is not feasible;

(c)   suspend her from work. The Employment Rights Act 1996 (which is the responsibility of the Department of Trade and Industry) requires that this suspension should be on full pay. Employment rights are enforced through the employment tribunals.

95   All employers should take account of women of child-bearing age when carrying out the risk assessment and identify the preventive and protective measures that are required in Regulation 3. The additional steps of altering working conditions or hours of work, offering suitable alternative work or suspension as outlined above may be taken once an employee has given her employer notice in writing that she is pregnant, has given birth within the last six months or is breastfeeding. If the employee continues to breastfeed for more than six months after the birth she should ensure the employer is informed of this, so that the appropriate measures can continue to be taken. Employers need to ensure that those workers who are breastfeeding are not exposed to risks that could damage their health and safety as long as they breastfeed. If the employee informs her employer that she is pregnant for the purpose of any other statutory requirements, such as statutory maternity pay, this will be sufficient for the purpose of these Regulations.

96   Once an employer has been informed in writing that an employee is a new or expectant mother, the employer needs to immediately put into place the steps described in paragraph 94 and 95. The employer may request confirmation of the pregnancy by means of a certificate from a registered medical practitioner or a registered midwife in writing. If this certificate has not been produced within a reasonable period of time, the employer is not bound to maintain changes to working hours or conditions or to maintain paid leave. A reasonable period of time will allow for all necessary medical examinations and tests to be completed.

97   Further guidance on new and expectant mothers is contained in *New and expectant mothers at work: A guide for employers* (see References and further reading section). The table of hazards identified in the EC Directive on Pregnant Workers (92/85/EEC) is given in this publication, along with the risks and ways to avoid them. The DTI booklet *PL705 Suspension from work on medical or maternity grounds* and *PL958 Maternity rights,* both of which cover the maternity suspension provisions, are available from DTI.

Regulation 19

Protection of young persons

Regulation

(1)   Every employer shall ensure that young persons employed by him are protected at work from any risks to their health or safety which are a consequence of their lack of experience, or absence of awareness of existing or potential risks or the fact that young persons have not yet fully matured.

(2)   Subject to paragraph (3), no employer shall employ a young person for work -

(a)   which is beyond his physical or psychological capacity;

(b)   involving harmful exposure to agents which are toxic or carcinogenic, cause heritable genetic damage or harm to the unborn child or which in any other way chronically affect human health;

(c)   involving harmful exposure to radiation;

(d)   involving the risk of accidents which it may reasonably be assumed cannot be recognised or avoided by young persons owing to their insufficient attention to safety or lack of experience or training; or

(e)   in which there is a risk to health from:-

(i)   extreme cold or heat;

(ii)   noise; or

(iii)   vibration,

and in determining whether work will involve harm or risks for the purposes of this paragraph, regard shall be had to the results of the assessment.

(3)   Nothing in paragraph (2) shall prevent the employment of a young person who is no longer a child for work-

(a)   where it is necessary for his training;

(b)   where the young person will be supervised by a competent person; and

(c)   where any risk will be reduced to the lowest level that is reasonably practicable.

(4)   The provisions contained in this regulation are without prejudice to-

(a)   the provisions contained elsewhere in these Regulations; and

(b)   any prohibition or restriction, arising otherwise than by this regulation, on the employment of any person.

19

ACOP

98   **The employer needs to carry out the risk assessment before young workers start work and to see where risk remains, taking account of control measures in place, as described in regulation 3. For young workers, the risk assessment needs to pay attention to areas of risk described in regulation 19(2). For several of these areas the employer will need to assess the risks with the control measures in place under other statutory requirements.**

99   **When control measures have been taken against these risks and if a significant risk still remains, no child (young worker under the compulsory school age) can be employed to do this work. A young**

19

34

worker, above the minimum school leaving age, cannot do this work unless:

(a) it is necessary for his or her training; and

(b) she or he is supervised by a competent person; and

(c) the risk will be reduced to the lowest level reasonably practicable.

100 **Further guidance on young workers is contained in** *Young people at work: A guide for employers* **(see References and further reading section). The table on hazards, risks and ways of avoiding them from the EC Directive on the protection of Young People at Work (94/33/EEC) is given in this publication.**

Exemption certificates

(1) The Secretary of State for Defence may, in the interests of national security, by a certificate in writing exempt-

   (a) any of the home forces, any visiting force or any headquarters from those requirements of these Regulations which impose obligations other than those in regulations 16-18 on employers; or

   (b) any member of the home forces, any member of a visiting force or any member of a headquarters from the requirements imposed by regulation 14;

and any exemption such as is specified in sub-paragraph (a) or (b) of this paragraph may be granted subject to conditions and to a limit of time and may be revoked by the said Secretary of State by a further certificate in writing at any time.

(2) In this regulation-

   (a) "the home forces" has the same meaning as in section 12(1) of the Visiting Forces Act 1952[a];

   (b) "headquarters" means a headquarters for the time being specified in Schedule 2 to the Visiting Forces and International Headquarters (Application of Law) Order 1999[b];

   (c) "member of a headquarters" has the same meaning as in paragraph 1(1) of the Schedule to the International Headquarters and Defence Organisations Act 1964[c]; and

   (d) "visiting force" has the same meaning as it does for the purposes of any provision of Part I of the Visiting Forces Act 1952.

[a] *1952 c.67.*
[b] *S.I. 1999/1736.*
[c] *1964/c. 5.*

Provisions as to liability

Nothing in the relevant statutory provisions shall operate so as to afford an employer a defence in any criminal proceedings for a contravention of those provisions by reason of any act or default of-

   (a) an employee of his, or

   (b) a person appointed by him under regulation 7.

outbreak and spread of fire; and

(b) in respect of every part of the mine other than any building on the surface of that mine-

(i) include the designation of persons to implement the plan, ensuring that the number of such persons, their training and the equipment available to them is adequate, taking into account the size of, and the specific hazards involved in the mine concerned; and

(ii) include the arrangements for any necessary contacts with external emergency services, particularly as regards rescue work and fire-fighting; and

(iii) be adapted to the nature of the activities carried on at that mine, the size of the mine and take account of the persons other than employees who may be present".

[a]*S.I. 1995/2005.*

106 Regulation 26 introduces a new paragraph into regulation 4 of the Mines Miscellaneous Health and Safety Provisions Regulations 1995. This requires that a fire protection plan be included in all cases in the health and safety document required by these Regulations. In all parts of the mine other than buildings on the surface, the mine owner is required to designate in the document those who are to implement the plan and include the arrangements for the necessary contacts with external services, especially rescue work and fire-fighting.

Regulation 27

Amendment of the Construction (Health, Safety and Welfare) Regulations 1996

(1) The Construction (Health, Safety and Welfare) Regulations 1996[a] shall be amended in accordance with the following provision of this regulation.

(2) Paragraph (2) of regulation 20 shall be deleted and the following substituted -

" (2) Without prejudice to the generality of paragraph (1), arrangements prepared pursuant to that paragraph shall -
(a) have regard to those matters set out in paragraph (4) of regulation 19;

(b) designate an adequate number of persons who will implement the arrangements; and

(c) include any necessary contacts with external emergency services, particularly as regards rescue work and fire-fighting.".

[a]*S.I. 1996/1592.*

107 This regulation amends regulation 20 of the Construction (Health, Safety and Welfare) Regulations 1996, so that arrangements for dealing with foreseeable emergencies on construction sites include designating people to implement the arrangements and arranging necessary contacts with external services, especially rescue work and fire-fighting.

Regulation 28

Regulations to have effect as health and safety regulations

Subject to regulation 9 of the Fire Precautions (Workplace) Regulations 1997[(a)], these Regulations shall, to the extent that they would not otherwise do so, have effect as if they were health and safety regulations within the meaning of Part I of the Health and Safety at Work etc. Act 1974.

[(a)]*S.I. 1997/1840; amended by S.I. 1999/1877.*

Regulation 29

Revocations and consequential amendments

(1)   The Management of Health and Safety at Work Regulations 1992[(a)], the Management of Health and Safety at Work (Amendment) Regulations 1994[(b)], the Health and Safety (Young Persons) Regulations 1997[(c)] and Part III of the Fire Precautions (Workplace) Regulations 1997 are hereby revoked.

(2)   The instruments specified in column 1 of Schedule 2 shall be amended in accordance with the corresponding provisions in column 3 of that Schedule.

[(a)]*S.I. 1992/2051; amended by S.I. 1994/2865; S.I. 1997/135, and S.I. 1997/1840.*
[(b)]*S.I. 1994/2865.*
[(c)]*S.I. 1997/135.*

Regulation 30

Transitional provision

The substitution of provisions in these Regulations for provisions of the Management of Health and Safety at Work Regulations 1992 shall not affect the continuity of the law; and accordingly anything done under or for the purposes of such provision of the 1992 Regulations shall have effect as if done under or for the purposes of any corresponding provision of these Regulations.

General principles of prevention

Regulation 4

(This Schedule specifies the general principles of prevention set out in Article 6(2) of Council Directive 89/391/EEC) [34]

(a)   *avoiding risks;*

(b)   *evaluating the risks which cannot be avoided;*

(c)   *combating the risks at source;*

(d)   *adapting the work to the individual, especially as regards the design of workplaces, the choice of work equipment and the choice of working and production methods, with a view, in particular, to alleviating monotonous work and work at a predetermined work-rate and to reducing their effect on health;*

(e)   *adapting to technical progress;*

(f)   *replacing the dangerous by the non-dangerous or the less dangerous;*

(g)   *developing a coherent overall prevention policy which covers technology, organisation of work, working conditions, social relationships and the influence of factors relating to the working environment;*

(h)   *giving collective protective measures priority over individual protective measures; and*

(i)   *giving appropriate instructions to employees.*

[34] *OJ No. L183, 29.6.89, p.1.*

Consequential Amendments

Regulation 29

Column 1 *Description of Instrument*	Column 2 *References*	Column 3 *Extent of Modification*
The Safety Representatives and Safety Committees Regulations 1977	S.I. 1977/500; amended by S.I. 1992/2051; S.I. 1996/1513; S.I. 1997/1840; S.I. 1999/860 and by section 1(1) and (2) of the Employment Rights (Dispute Resolution) Act 1998.	In regulation 4A(1)(b) for "regulations 6(1) and 7(1)(b) of the Management of Health and Safety at Work Regulations 1992", there shall be substituted "regulations 7(1) and 8(1)(b) of the Management of Health and Safety at Work Regulations 1999;".
The Offshore Installations (Safety Representatives and Safety Committees) Regulations 1989	S.I. 1989/971; amended by S.I. 1992/2885; S.I. 1993/1823; S.I. 1995/738; S.I. 1995/743; and S.I. 1995/3163.	In regulation 23(4) for "regulation 6(1) of the Management of Health and Safety at Work Regulations 1992", there shall be substituted "regulation 7(1) of the Management of Health and Safety at Work Regulations 1999".
The Railways (Safety Case) Regulations 1994	S.I. 1994/237; amended by S.I. 1996/1592.	In paragraph 6 of Schedule 1 for "regulation 3 of the Management of Health and Safety at Work Regulations 1992 and particulars of the arrangements he has made pursuant to regulation 4(1) thereof.", there shall be substituted "regulation 3 of the Management of Health and Safety at Work Regulations 1999 and particulars of the arrangements he has made in accordance with regulation 5(1) thereof.".
The Suspension from Work (on Maternity Grounds) Order 1994*	S.I. 1994/2930.	In article 1(2)(b) for ""the 1992 Regulations" means the Management of Health and Safety at Work

Column 1 *Description of Instrument*	Column 2 *References*	Column 3 *Extent of Modification*
		Regulations 1992", there shall be substituted, ""the 1999 Regulations" means the Management of Health and Safety at Work Regulations 1999"; and
		In article 2(b) for "regulation 13B of the 1992 regulations", there shall be substituted "regulation 17 of the 1999 Regulations".
The Construction (Design and Management) Regulations 1994	S.I. 1994/3140; amended by S.I. 1996/1592.	In regulation 16(1)(a) for "regulation 9 of the Management of Health and Safety at Work Regulations 1992", there shall be substituted "regulation 11 of the Management of Health and Safety at Work Regulations 1999;";
		In regulation 17(2)(a) for "regulation 8 of the Management of Health and Safety at Work Regulations 1992;", there shall be substituted "regulation 10 of the Management of Health and Safety at Work Regulations 1999;";
		In regulation 17(2)(b) for "regulation 11(2)(b) of the Management of Health and Safety at Work Regulations 1992", there shall be substituted "regulation 13(2)(b) of the Management of Health and Safety at Work Regulations 1999"; and
		In regulation 19(1)(b) for "the Management

Column 1 Description of Instrument	Column 2 References	Column 3 Extent of Modification
		of Health and Safety at Work Regulations 1992", there shall be substituted "the Management of Health and Safety at Work Regulations 1999".
The Escape and Rescue from Mines Regulations 1995	S.I. 1995/2870.	In regulation 2(1) for ""the 1992 Regulations" means the Management of Health and Safety at Work Regulations 1992", there shall be substituted ""the 1999 Regulations" means the Management of Health and Safety at Work Regulations 1999"; and
		In regulation 4(2) for "regulation 3 of the 1992 Regulations," there shall be substituted "regulation 3 of the 1999 Regulations.".
The Mines Miscellaneous Health and Safety Provisions Regulations 1995	S.I. 1995/2005.	In regulation 2(1) for ""the 1992 regulations" means the Management of Health and Safety at Work Regulations 1992;", there shall be substituted ""the 1999 Regulations" means the Management of Health and Safety at Work Regulations 1999;" and
		In regulation 4(1)(a) for "regulation 3 of the 1992 Regulations;", there shall be substituted "regulation 3 of the 1999 Regulations;".
The Quarries Miscellaneous Health and Safety Provisions Regulations 1995	S.I. 1995/2036.	In regulation 2(1) for ""the 1992 Regulations" means the Management of Health and Safety at Work Regulations 1992;", there shall be substituted ""the 1999

Schedule

Column 1 *Description of Instrument*	Column 2 *References*	Column 3 *Extent of Modification*
The Control of Lead at Work Regulations 1998	S.I. 1998/543.	In regulation 5 for "regulation 3 of the Management of Health and Safety at Work Regulations 1992", there shall be substituted "regulation 3 of the Management of Health and Safety at Work Regulations 1999".
The Working Time Regulations 1998*	S.I. 1998/1833.	In regulation 6(8)(b) for "regulation 3 of the Management of Health and Safety at Work Regulations 1992", there shall be substituted "regulation 3 of the Management of Health and Safety at Work Regulations 1999".
The Quarries Regulations 1999	S.I. 1999/2024.	In regulation 2(1) for ""the 1992 Regulations" means the Management of Health and Safety at Work Regulations 1992;", there shall be substituted ""the 1999 Regulations" means the Management of Health and Safety at Work Regulations 1999;". In regulation 7(1)(a) for "paragraphs (1) to (3c) of regulation 3 of the 1992 Regulations;" there shall be substituted "regulation 3 of the Management of Health and Safety at Work Regulations 1999". In regulation 43 for "regulation 5 of the 1992 regulations" there shall be substituted "regulation 6 of the 1999 Regulations".

Note

The Regulations marked with an asterisk are referred to in the Preamble to these Regulations

2

References and further reading

A guide to the Health and Safety (Consultation with Employees) Regulations 1996. Guidance on Regulations L95 HSE Books 1996 ISBN 0 7176 1234 1

BS 8800:2004 *Occupational health and safety management systems. Guide* British Standards Institution 2004 ISBN 0 580 43987 9

Charity and voluntary workers: A guide to health and safety at work HSG192 HSE Books 1999 ISBN 0 7176 2424 2

Reducing risks, protecting people Discussion Document DDE11 HSE 1999 Web only version available at http://www.hse.gov.uk/consult/disdocs/dde11.htm

EC Directive on Pregnant Workers (92/85/EEC) *Official Journal of the European Communities* 28 November 1992, 35, L348, pp.1-7

EC Directive on the protection of young people at work (94/33/EEC) *Official Journal of the European Communities* 20 August 1994, 37, L216, pp.12-20

Fire safety: An employers guide Guidance Booklet HSE Books 1999 ISBN 0 11 341229 0

Five steps to risk assessment Leaflet INDG163(rev1) HSE Books 1998 (single copy free or priced packs of 10 ISBN 0 7176 1565 0)

Health surveillance at work HSG61 (Second edition) HSE Books 1999 ISBN 0 7176 1705 X

Homeworking: Guidance for employers and employees on health and safety Leaflet INDG226 HSE Books 1996 (single copy free or priced packs of 15 ISBN 0 7176 1204 X)

New and expectant mothers at work: A guide for employers HSG122 (Second edition) HSE Books 2002 ISBN 0 7176 2583 4

Safety representatives and safety committees L87 (Third edition) HSE Books 1996 ISBN 0 7176 1220 1

Need help on health and safety? Guidance for employers on when and how to get advice on health and safety Leaflet INDG322 HSE Books 2000 (single copy free or priced packs of 10 ISBN 0 7176 1790 4)

Successful health and safety management HSG65 (Second edition) HSE Books 1997 ISBN 0 7176 1276 7

Suspension from work on medical or maternity grounds under health and safety regulations Booklet URN 01/690 Department of Trade and Industry 1998

First aid at work. The Health and Safety (First Aid) Regulations 1981. Approved Code of Practice and guidance L74 HSE Books 1997 ISBN 0 7176 1050 0

Understanding health surveillance at work: An introduction for employers Leaflet INDG304 HSE Books 1999 (single copy free or priced packs of 15 ISBN 0 7176 1712 2)

Young people at work: A guide for employers HSG165 (Second edition) HSE Books 2000 ISBN 0 7176 1889 7

British Standards are available from BSI Customer Services, 389 Chiswick High Road, London W4 4AL Tel: 020 8996 9001 Fax: 020 8996 7001 Website: www.bsi-global.com